The route to your roots

When they look back at their formative years, many Indians nostalgically recall the vital part Amar Chitra Katha picture books have played in their lives. It was **ACK – Amar Chitra Katha** – that first gave them a glimpse of their glorious heritage.

Since they were introduced in 1967, there are now **over 400 Amar Chitra Katha** titles to choose from. **Over 100 million copies** have been sold worldwide.

Now the Amar Chitra Katha titles are even more widely available in **1000+ bookstores all across India**. Log on to www.ack-media.com to locate a bookstore near you. If you do not have access to a bookstore, you can buy all the titles through our online store **www.amarchitrakatha.com**. We provide quick delivery anywhere in the world.

To make it easy for you to locate the titles of your choice from our treasure trove of titles, the books are now arranged in five categories.

Epics and Mythology
Best known stories from the Epics and the Puranas

Indian Classics
Enchanting tales from Indian literature

Fables and Humour
Evergreen folktales, legends and tales of wisdom and humour

Bravehearts
Stirring tales of brave men and women of India

Visionaries
Inspiring tales of thinkers, social reformers and nation builders

Contemporary Classics
The Best of Modern Indian literature

Amar Chitra Katha Pvt Ltd

© Amar Chitra Katha Pvt Ltd, 1998, Reprinted December 2017,
ISBN 978-81-89999-81-0
Published by Amar Chitra Katha Pvt. Ltd., AFL House, 7th Floor,
Lok Bharati Complex,Marol Maroshi Road, Andheri (East), Mumbai - 400059, India.
Printed at M/s Indigo Press (I) Pvt Ltd., Mumbai.
For Consumer Complaints Contact Tel : + 91-2249188881/2
Email: customerservice@ack-media.com

The route to your roots

KRISHNADEVA RAYA

The king of Vijayanagara, Vira Narasimha, was very ill. He was afraid that after his death, his much loved and popular brother, Krishnadeva Raya, would seize the throne from his little son. So he asked a trusted minister to put Krishnadeva to death. The conscience-stricken minister could not perform such a heinous deed and convinced the bewildered prince to escape. Fate had already decreed that Krishnadeva Raya would one day rule the Vijayanagara empire and take it to its zenith of glory.

Script
Subba Rao

Illustrations
G.R.Naik

Editor
Anant Pai

KRISHNADEVA RAYA

VIJAYANAGARA, FOUNDED IN 1336, ROSE TO THE ZENITH OF ITS PROSPERITY IN THE EARLY SIXTEENTH CENTURY.

IN 1509, VIRA NARASIMHA, KING OF VIJAYANAGARA, FELL SERIOUSLY ILL. IN THE CAPITAL, PEOPLE WONDERED WHO WOULD SUCCEED HIM.

THE KING MAY NOMINATE HIS LITTLE SON...

NEVER! NOT WHEN HIS BROTHER, THE ABLE KRISHNADEVA, IS ALIVE.

OUR KING KNOWS WHAT IS BEST FOR THE COUNTRY.

BUT AT THAT MOMENT THE KING WAS MORE CONCERNED ABOUT WHAT WAS BEST FOR HIS SON.

WILL YOU FULFIL MY LAST WISH, APPAJI*?

SPEAK OUT, YOUR MAJESTY.

MY SON WILL NEVER BE KING SO LONG AS KRISHNADEVA IS ALIVE.

* MINISTER THIMMARASU WAS AFFECTIONATELY ADDRESSED AS APPAJI.

2

KRISHNADEVA MUST DIE. PROMISE ME THAT YOU WILL PUT HIM TO DEATH.

WHAT! PUT KRISHNA TO DEATH!

AS THE UNHAPPY MINISTER WAS ABOUT TO LEAVE—

WAIT! AS A PROOF OF YOUR HAVING KILLED HIM, HIS EYES SHOULD BE SHOWN TO ME, TOMORROW.

AS YOU COMMAND, YOUR MAJESTY.

WHEN THIMMARASU CAME OUT, HE MET KRISHNADEVA.

HOW IS THE KING, APPAJI?

HE'S MUCH BETTER.

THEN THE MINISTER LOWERED HIS VOICE.

KRISHNA, ARE YOU PREPARED TO DIE FOR THE KING?

MOST CERTAINLY, APPAJI. THE KING IS THE COUNTRY AND I AM PREPARED TO DIE FOR MY COUNTRY.

THIMMARASU SPENT A SLEEPLESS NIGHT.

APPAJI, KRISHNADEVA MUST DIE.

I AM PREPARED TO DIE FOR MY COUNTRY.

THE NEXT DAY —

...COME ALONE AND IN SECRECY.

AS YOU WISH, APPAJI.

THAT NIGHT —

TAKE THIS HORSE, DISGUISE YOURSELF AND LEAVE THE CAPITAL.

WHY, APPAJI?

I'LL TELL YOU SOME OTHER TIME. NOW, MAKE HASTE AND GO. REMEMBER, NO ONE MUST KNOW WHO YOU ARE.

YOU CAN TRUST ME.

AND KRISHNADEVA LEFT.

THIMMARASU THEN HAD A GOAT KILLED AND BROUGHT ITS EYES TO THE KING.

KRISHNA IS NO MORE, YOUR MAJESTY. HERE ARE HIS EYES.

MY SON AND I WILL FOREVER BE INDEBTED TO YOU, APPAJI.

DAYS LATER, WHILE WANDERING INCOGNITO, KRISHNADEVA HAPPENED TO VISIT A TEMPLE WHERE CHINNADEVI, THE TEMPLE DANCER, WAS PERFORMING.

WHAT A DIVINE BEAUTY! SHE LOOKS LIKE A LOTUS THAT HAS JUST BLOS- SOMED.

AFTER THE DANCE—

WHY ARE YOU STILL HERE? WHY DON'T YOU GO HOME?

I HAVE NOWHERE TO GO.

CHINNADEVI TOOK HIM HOME WITH HER.

MOTHER, THIS MAN HAS NO HOME. SO I BROUGHT HIM HERE.

THEN MAKE THIS YOUR OWN HOME, SON.

WHAT IS YOUR NAME, STRANGER?

I HAVE NO NAME.

CHINNADEVI DID NOT PRESS HIM FURTHER.

SO YOU KNOW HOW TO WIELD A BOW!

WATCH ME, STRANGER; AND WATCH THAT BIRD.

SHE SHOT DOWN THE BIRD. KRISHNADEVA WAS AMAZED.

YOU ARE A GOOD SHOT, INDEED, CHINNA!

AND YOU ARE A COWARD, AFRAID EVEN TO DISCLOSE YOUR NAME!

A FEW DAYS LATER —

MUST YOU LEAVE?

I MUST. GOD WILLING, I'LL SEE YOU AGAIN.

MEANWHILE, THE SUDDEN DISAPPEARANCE OF KRISHNADEVA DID NOT GO UNNOTICED IN THE CAPITAL.

WHY ISN'T THE PRINCE SEEN ANYWHERE?

HAS HE BEEN DONE TO DEATH?

GOD FORBID!

THE NEWS OF VIRA NARASIMHA'S ILLNESS AND KRISHNADEVA'S DISAPPEARANCE REACHED GULBARGA, THE CAPITAL OF MAHMOOD SHAH, THE BAHMANI KING.

NOW IS THE TIME TO ATTACK VIJAYANAGARA AND MAKE IT OURS.

WHAT IF THE KING DIES AND KRISHNADEVA REAPPEARS TO SUCCEED HIM, YOUR MAJESTY?

THEN WE'LL TAKE ADVANTAGE OF HIS INEXPERIENCE.

A FEW DAYS LATER, AT VIJAYANAGARA —

YOUR MAJESTY, THE BAHMANI KING IS PLANNING TO INVADE OUR EMPIRE.

MY KINGDOM IS IN DANGER! I MUST LEAD MY MEN...

YOUR MAJESTY, COMPOSE YOURSELF. YOU ARE NOT FIT TO WALK EVEN A FEW STEPS.

ALAS! I AM AN INVALID. THE PRINCE IS A MERE CHILD. AND KRISHNA, WHO COULD HAVE ABLY DEFENDED THE KINGDOM, IS NO MORE. APPAJI, WHY DID YOU LET ME HAVE MY WAY?

THIS IS THE RIGHT TIME FOR KRISHNADEVA TO COME BACK.

KRISHNADEVA IS ALIVE, YOUR MAJESTY. FORGIVE ME, I DID NOT OBEY YOUR COMMAND.

FORGIVE YOU, APPAJI? I AM INDEBTED TO YOU! YOU HAVE SAVED ME FROM THE SIN OF KILLING A BROTHER.

LATER, WHEN THIMMARASU BROUGHT KRISHNADEVA TO MEET THE KING —

KRISHNA, FORGIVE ME. I HAVE DONE YOU A GREAT WRONG. AFTER ME, YOU MUST SHOULDER THE BURDEN OF RULING THE KINGDOM.

LET BYGONES BE BYGONES, YOUR MAJESTY.

WHEN THE AILING **KING** DIED, THE COUNCILLORS DECIDED TO CROWN KRISHNADEVA **AS THE** EMPEROR.

KRISHNADEVA, CUSTOM REQUIRES THAT YOU BE MARRIED BEFORE THE CORONATION.

THEN, APPAJI, I WILL SHOW YOU THE GIRL WHO HAS WON MY HEART.

THE NEXT DAY HE TOOK THE ELDERLY MINISTER TO THE TEMPLE OF VIRUPAKSHA.

ISN'T SHE LOVELY, APPAJI?

BUT A TEMPLE DANCER CAN'T BE THE QUEEN OF VIJAYANAGARA!

KRISHNADEVA, HOWEVER, WAS FIRM IN HIS RESOLVE.

APPAJI, I MET HER WHILE TRAVELLING INCOGNITO. I HAD NO NAME, HOME OR FORTUNE AND YET SHE GAVE HER HEART TO ME. I'D RATHER GIVE UP THE KING-DOM THAN DEAR CHINNA.

WE WILL SEE WHAT CAN BE DONE TO RECONCILE THE DICTATES OF TRADI-TION✱ AND THE DICTATES OF YOUR HEART.

✱ THE FIRST WIFE OF A KING SHOULD BE A WOMAN OF NOBLE BIRTH.

FINALLY, KRISHNADEVA RAYA ACCEPTED TIRUMALA DEVI, A ROYAL PRINCESS, AS HIS FIRST QUEEN···

··· AND WAS CROWNED EMPEROR OF VIJAYANAGARA ON AUGUST 8, 1509.

SOON AFTER THE CORONATION, HE MARRIED HIS BELOVED, CHINNADEVI.

MEANWHILE, THE BAHMANI KING HAD COMPLETED THE PREPARATION FOR THE CAMPAIGN AND REACHED DIWANI WHERE KRISHNADEVA RAYA GAVE HIM BATTLE.

NO, WE CANNOT FIGHT KRISHNADEVA RAYA.

THE BAHMANI ARMY HAD TO BEAT A HASTY RETREAT.

KRISHNADEVA IS AFTER US!

FLEE!

LATER, KRISHNADEVA RAYA ADDRESSED HIS ARMY.

OUR VICTORY SHOULD NOT MAKE US COMPLACENT. PRATAPA RUDRA OF KALINGA AND ADIL KHAN OF BIJAPUR ARE OUR SWORN ENEMIES. ONLY WHEN THEY ARE DEFEATED, WILL OUR KINGDOM KNOW PEACE. SO, FOR THE SAKE OF PEACE, WE MUST SUBDUE THEM.

... REACHED UDAIGIRI, SCALED THE FORT AND ATTACKED!

TIRUMALA RAUT COULD NOT HOLD OUT FOR LONG.

YOUR MAJESTY, TIRUMALA RAUT, OUR CHIEF, HAS SENT HIS TURBAN AS A TOKEN OF SURRENDER.

THEN ON WE GO TO FORT KONDAVIDU!

BUT THE VIJAYANAGARA ARMY, ON REACHING KONDAVIDU, FOUND IT HARD TO SCALE THE STRONG FORT.

THE WALL IS STEEP; AND OUR ARROWS DON'T REACH FAR ENOUGH TO KILL OUR ENEMIES.

HAVE BAMBOO SCAFFOLDS ERECTED AROUND THE FORT.

THE VIJAYANAGARA SOLDIERS GOT DOWN TO WORK. AS SOON AS THE SCAFFOLDS ROSE AS HIGH AS THE FORT —

WATCH, APPAJI! WATCH THIS BLAZING ARROW PIERCE THE VERY HEART OF KONDAVIDU.

THE ARROW FOUND ITS MARK. HEAPS OF GRAIN DEEP WITHIN THE FORT, CAUGHT FIRE.

LOOK! THEY'VE SET FIRE TO THE GRAIN.

FORGET THE GRAIN. THEY'VE ALMOST ENTERED THE FORT. LET'S FIGHT THEM OFF.

IN THE CONFUSION THAT FOLLOWED, KRISHNADEVA AND HIS ARMY ENTERED THE FORT AND EFFORTLESSLY TOOK IT.

AT POTANUR, PRATAPA RUDRA WAS WORRIED.

KRISHNADEVA IS NOW LIKE A TIGER THAT HAS TASTED HUMAN BLOOD.

WE NEED NOT WORRY. THE SIXTEEN LOYAL CHIEFTAINS HAVE PROMISED THEIR SUPPORT, MY LORD.

THE SIXTEEN CHIEFTAINS SOON ARRIVED AT POTANUR.

LEAVE ALONE KRISHNADEVA, NOT EVEN AN EARTHQUAKE WILL SHAKE US FROM THE FORT.

WE APPRECIATE YOUR COURAGE. AND WE TREASURE YOUR LOYALTY TO THE THRONE.

PRATAPA RUDRA WENT ROUND THE FORT ON AN INSPECTION TOUR.

REINFORCE THIS SECTION. IT DOESN'T LOOK SOUND.

YES, YOUR MAJESTY.

WE HAVE ENOUGH STOCK TO LAST A YEAR, YOUR MAJESTY.

SEE THAT THERE IS PROPER DISTRIBUTION AND NO WASTAGE.

THUS PRATAPA RUDRA WAS FULLY PREPARED WHEN KRISHNADEVA RAYA LAID SIEGE TO POTANUR.

THE BATTLE CONTINUED FOR MONTHS. KRISHNADEVA RAYA WAS WORRIED.

A HUNDRED DAYS WE'VE FOUGHT. BUT THE FORT IS NOT YET OURS, APPAJI.

WE SHOULD RESORT TO STRATAGEM, YOUR MAJESTY.

THIMMARASU WROTE A LETTER TO HIS SECRET AGENT INSIDE THE FORT.

HE THEN TIED THE LETTER TO THE FOOT OF A HOMING PIGEON, AND SET IT FREE.

THE BIRD FLEW STRAIGHT TO THE AGENT.

WELCOME HOME! AND WHAT HAVE YOU HERE?

THE SECRET AGENT HAD A MEETING WITH HIS ASSOCIATES.

WE WILL CARRY OUT THE ORDERS TOMORROW NIGHT. IT SHOULD BE WELL-TIMED —WHEN PRATAPA RUDRA MAKES HIS ROUNDS.

AT MIDNIGHT THE NEXT DAY —

STOP! WHAT ARE YOU CARRYING? OPEN THE BOXES.

THE MEN WERE TAKEN TO AN ARMY GUARD POST WHERE THE BOXES WERE OPENED.

DIAMONDS!! TO WHOM WERE THEY GOING? SPEAK UP!

MEANWHILE, KING PRATAPA RUDRA CAME THERE.

WHAT'S GOING ON HERE?

YOUR MAJESTY, THESE MEN WERE CAUGHT CARRYING DIAMONDS AND A LETTER THAT MAKES NO SENSE.

THE KING READ THE LETTER.

TRUSTED FRIEND, THIS IS THE SECOND CONSIGNMENT. ONE MORE WILL BE SENT AS SOON AS YOU AND YOUR FRIENDS ACCOMPLISH YOUR MISSION AT THE APPOINTED TIME ...

BUT PRATAPA RUDRA SOON REALISED THAT DISCRETION WAS THE BETTER PART OF VALOUR.

THEY ARE SIXTEEN, AND I AM ALONE. I SHOULD RUN BEFORE THEY CAPTURE ME AND TAKE ME TO KRISHNADEVA.

MEANWHILE, A GUARD CAME RUNNING TO THE CHIEFTAINS.

THE KING IS FURIOUS. HE CAUGHT THE MEN WHO WERE CARRYING A GIFT OF DIAMONDS FOR YOU FROM KRISHNADEVA RAYA.

NONSENSE! FROM KRISHNADEVA RAYA? FOR ME? SHEER NONSENSE!

LET US GO TO OUR KING AND EXPLAIN.

WHAT IF HE REFUSES TO BELIEVE US?

SUPPOSING HE THROWS US INTO PRISON? THIS IS HIS TERRITORY.

IT WOULD BE PRUDENT TO ESCAPE FROM HERE WHILE WE CAN.

THE SIXTEEN CHIEFTAINS QUIETLY SLIPPED AWAY FROM THE FORT WITH THEIR MEN.

AND KRISHNADEVA RAYA MARCHED TRIUMPHANTLY INTO POTANUR. THIMMARASU'S RUSE HAD PAID OFF.

VICTORY TO KRISHNADEVA RAYA!

LATER, PEACE WAS DECLARED BETWEEN VIJAYANAGARA AND KALINGA. KRISHNADEVA RAYA MARRIED JAGANMOHINI, THE KALINGA PRINCESS.

MEANWHILE, AFTER THE DEATH OF MAHMOOD SHAH, THE BAHMANI KING OF THE DECCAN, ISMAIL ADIL KHAN, HAD DECLARED HIMSELF THE INDEPENDENT RULER OF BIJAPUR.

WE'LL TAKE GULBARGA AND IMPRISON THE INCOMPETENT SONS OF MAHMOOD SHAH.

KRISHNADEVA RAYA RETURNED TO HIS CAPITAL AND FOUND THAT ADIL KHAN HAD TAKEN RAICHUR WHILE HE WAS AWAY.

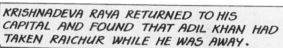

WE WILL HAVE TO DECLARE WAR AGAINST HIM.

WE NEED HORSES.

SIDDI MERCAR, AN OFFICER IN THE COURT OF VIJAYANAGARA, WAS SUMMONED.

GO TO THE PORTUGUESE AND BUY HORSES WORTH 40,000 PAGODAS FROM THEM.

MANY DAYS PASSED. SIDDI MERCAR DID NOT RETURN. THEN SPIES CAME WITH NEWS.

SIDDI MERCAR HAS FLED WITH THE 40,000 PAGODAS TO BIJAPUR, YOUR MAJESTY.

THIS IS TREASON. SEND AN AMBASSADOR TO BIJAPUR REQUESTING ADIL KHAN TO REPATRIATE SIDDI MERCAR.

A FEW DAYS LATER, THE AMBASSADOR RETURNED FROM BIJAPUR.

YOUR MAJESTY, THE RULER OF BIJAPUR PROFESSES THAT HE DOES NOT KNOW THE WHEREABOUTS OF SIDDI MERCAR.

HE IS ASKING FOR TROUBLE. WE'LL MARCH AGAINST HIM AFTER WE TAKE RAICHUR WHICH RIGHTFULLY BELONGS TO US.

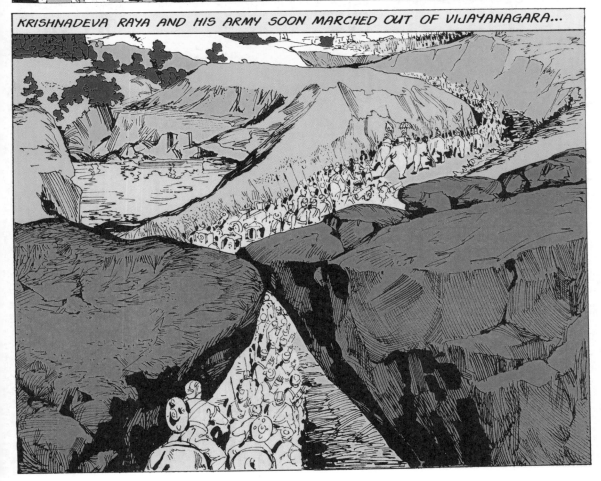

KRISHNADEVA RAYA AND HIS ARMY SOON MARCHED OUT OF VIJAYANAGARA...

...AND LAID SIEGE TO RAICHUR.

AS SOON AS HE LEARNT OF THIS, ADIL KHAN RUSHED TO THE DEFENCE OF RAICHUR. HE CAMPED ON THE BANK OF THE RIVER KRISHNA.

THE NEWS SOON REACHED KRISHNADEVA RAYA.

YOUR MAJESTY, ADIL KHAN HAS CROSSED THE KRISHNA RIVER AND WILL BE ATTACKING US FROM THE REAR.

APPAJI, SEND PART OF OUR FORCES TO STOP ADIL KHAN. LET THE REST CONTINUE WITH THE SIEGE.

27

INSPIRED BY HIS WORDS, THE SOLDIERS FOUGHT WITH FRESH CONFIDENCE. NOW THE BIJAPUR ARMY WAS ON THE RUN WITH THE SOLDIERS OF VIJAYANAGARA IN HOT PURSUIT.

WHILE THOUSANDS OF HIS SOLDIERS AND HORSES FELL INTO THE RIVER WHICH WAS NOW IN SPATE, AND PERISHED, ADIL KHAN HIMSELF GOT AWAY ON AN ELEPHANT.

GOD, LET ME ESCAPE WITH MY LIFE!

THE ENEMY HAS LEFT BEHIND 40,000 HORSES, 1,000 ELEPHANTS, 400 CANNONS AND 900 GUN CARRIAGES.

GOOD! NOW ON TO RAICHUR.

KRISHNADEVA RAYA RETURNED TO THE SIEGE OF RAICHUR. AS LUCK WOULD HAVE IT, A PORTUGUESE FRIEND OF HIS HAPPENED TO PASS BY.

CHRISTOVO, DO YOU SEE HOW STRONG THAT FORT IS? IT'S WITHSTANDING OUR MOUNTING PRESSURE.

I'LL HELP YOU TAKE IT WITH MY MUSKET, YOUR MAJESTY.

CHRISTOVO AND HIS MUSKETEERS GUNNED DOWN THE GUARDS AND THE CHIEF OF THE FORT.

AND KRISHNADEVA RAYA AND HIS ARMY ENTERED RAICHUR.

ADIL KHAN SENT AN AMBASSADOR TO KRISHNADEVA RAYA.

OUR KING REQUESTS YOU TO GIVE BACK HIS TERRITORIES.

THAT I WILL, WHEN ADIL KHAN COMES TO ME AND FALLS AT MY FEET.

ADIL KHAN NATURALLY DIDN'T TURN UP. KRISHNADEVA RAYA'S ARMY MARCHED TOWARDS GULBARGA.

GULBARGA SOON FELL. KRISHNADEVA RAYA GAVE ASSURANCES TO THE CITIZENS.

YOUR LIVES AND PROPERTY WILL COME TO NO HARM.

MAY GOD BLESS YOU, YOUR MAJESTY.

THE FIRST THING KRISHNADEVA RAYA DID AT GULBARGA WAS TO SET FREE THE THREE SONS OF MAHMOOD SHAH, THE BAHMANI KING.

ADIL KHAN, OUR OWN GOVERNOR AT BIJAPUR, KEPT US CAPTIVE AFTER THE DEATH OF OUR FATHER. AND YOU, OUR SWORN ENEMY, HAVE FREED US.

PRINCE, VIJAYANAGARA AND THE BAHMANI KINGDOM ARE NEIGHBOURS. WE SHOULD LIVE IN PEACE AND FRIENDSHIP.

KRISHNADEVA RAYA MADE THE FIRST SON OF MAHMOOD SHAH, THE BAHMANI KING OF THE DECCAN.

WE ARE GRATEFUL TO THE EMPEROR OF VIJAYANAGARA FOR HIS KINDNESS.

ON HIS RETURN TO VIJAYANAGARA, KRISHNADEVA RAYA VISITED THE TEMPLE OF VIRUPAKSHA.

LORD, BY YOUR GRACE, I COULD REALISE MY FATHER'S DREAM OF TAKING UDAIGIRI AND RAICHUR. LORD, CONTINUE TO BE KIND TO YOUR HUMBLE SERVANT.

IN A SHORT SPAN OF 20 YEARS, KRISHNADEVA RAYA MADE VIJAYANAGARA STRONG AND PROSPEROUS.

CELEBRATING

50

AMAR CHITRA KATHA

YEARS

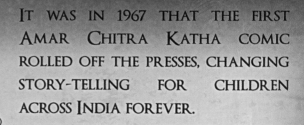

It was in 1967 that the first Amar Chitra Katha comic rolled off the presses, changing story-telling for children across India forever.

Five decades and more than 400 books later, we are still sharing stories from India's rich heritage, primarily because of the love and support shown by readers like yourself.

SO, FROM US TO YOU, HERE'S A BIG
THANK YOU!

ASHOKA

THE WARRIOR WHO SPOKE OF PEACE

The route to your roots

ASHOKA

A power-hungry warrior and a peace-loving wife – could they ever tread together on the path of non-violence? Ashoka waged war after ruthless war, yet by the time his children grew up, he proudly saw them off as Buddhist missionaries. Read about the charmed life of this famous king of Magadha, who not only built a prosperous kingdom but spread the message of universal love.

Script
Meena Talim

Illustrations
Ram Waeerkar

Editor
Anant Pai

ASHOKA

ASHOKA WAS THE SON OF KING BINDUSARA WHO RULED INDIA FROM HIS CAPITAL OF PATALIPUTRA IN THE THIRD CENTURY B.C. HE EXCELLED HIS BROTHERS IN THE ART OF WAR. THEREFORE, WHEN A REBELLION BROKE OUT IN THE DISTANT PROVINCE OF TAXILA, HE WAS SENT TO SUPPRESS IT.

WEEKS LATER –

YOUR MAJESTY! WE HAVE HAPPY NEWS HERE. ASHOKA HAS SUCCESSFULLY PUT DOWN THE REBELS.

HE SHALL RULE THERE AS THE VICEROY. HE WILL KEEP PEACE THERE.

BINDUSARA HAD A HUNDRED SONS BESIDES ASHOKA. THEY WERE NOT HAPPY TO HEAR THE NEWS.

ASHOKA HAS ALWAYS BEEN PROUD. THE SUCCESS WILL GO TO HIS HEAD.

IT WILL MAKE HIM MORE ARROGANT.

THAT IS EXACTLY WHAT WORRIES ME. ASHOKA IS RUTHLESS. HE MAY FIGHT WITH HIS BROTHERS FOR THE THRONE.

JUST THEN—

THERE IS A MESSENGER FROM UJJAINI, YOUR MAJESTY.

A REBELLION — THIS TIME IN UJJAINI.

SEND FOR ASHOKA.

ASHOKA'S MESSENGER SOON RETURNED.

SIR! SHE IS THE DAUGHTER OF A REPUTED SHRESHTHI'S* FAMILY.

TELL THE SHRESHTHI! I WANT TO MEET HIM.

MERCHANT

LATER—

SHRESHTHI, IF YOU PLEASE, I...

SIR, IS THERE ANYTHING YOU WANT ME TO DO FOR YOU?

I'VE NEVER SEEN OUR PRINCE HESITATE THUS.

I...YES. I WANT THE HAND OF YOUR DAUGHTER IN MARRIAGE.

I AM HONOURED, SIR.

AFTER A QUICK WEDDING, HE PROCEEDED TOWARDS UJJAINI ALONG WITH VIDISHA.

ASHOKA, A GREAT WARRIOR, IN NO TIME ROUTED THE REBELS.

THE REBELS LAID DOWN THEIR ARMS.

THE PEOPLE OF THE CITY GAVE ASHOKA A GRAND WELCOME.

IN THE PALACE GARDENS LATER—

THIS IS AN OCCASION FOR REJOICING, VIDISHA. BUT YOU LOOK SAD.

I DISLIKE KILLING... EVEN IN BATTLES... ESPECIALLY BY YOU.

THAT'S SILLY. YOU SAY IT, BECAUSE YOU ARE A BUDDHIST, I AM NOT.

*MAHI = WORLD

TWO YEARS LATER, VIDISHA GAVE BIRTH TO A DAUGHTER.

LORD! THIS TIME, LET ME CHOOSE THE NAME.

AS YOU WISH.

I'LL NAME HER SANGHA-MITRA.

OH, NO! THAT'S A BUDDHIST NAME.

ONE DAY, A MESSENGER CAME FROM PATALIPUTRA.

HIS MAJESTY HAS NOT BEEN KEEPING GOOD HEALTH. PLEASE RETURN TO PATALIPUTRA IMMEDIATELY.

ASHOKA HAD HURRIED CONSULTATIONS WITH VIDISHA.

I HAVE RECEIVED A MESSAGE FROM THE CHIEF MINISTER. MY FATHER IS ILL. I HAVE TO RUSH TO PATALIPUTRA...

...AND YOU AREN'T YET FIT TO ACCOMPANY ME.

WILL YOU STAY AT VIDISHA-NAGAR WITH YOUR PARENTS? I'LL SEND FOR YOU LATER.

AS YOU WISH, MY LORD!

TOGETHER THEY TRAVELLED UPTO VIDISHA-NAGAR.

PLEASE TAKE CARE OF YOUR HEALTH. AND DON'T PREACH NON-VIOLENCE TO MY MAHINDRA.

I WANT HIM TO BE A KING OF KINGS.

BEFORE I LEAVE, IS THERE ANYTHING YOU WANT ME TO DO?

YES. BUT GIVE ME YOUR WORD THAT YOU WILL.

I WILL. WHAT IS IT?

I WANT YOU TO SHUN VIOLENCE OF ALL KINDS.

AT PATALIPUTRA, ASHOKA WAS RECEIVED BY THE CHIEF MINISTER.

PRINCE! YOUR FATHER IS NO MORE. AND YOUR BROTHERS ARE FIGHTING AMONGST THEMSELVES FOR THE THRONE.

THE THRONE! IT IS MINE! I HAVE EARNED THE RIGHT TO IT.

ASHOKA FORGOT ALL ABOUT THE PROMISE HE HAD MADE TO VIDISHA.

ASHOKA WAS RUTHLESS IN KILLING ALL THOSE THAT CHALLENGED HIS RIGHT TO THE THRONE. SUMANADEVI, WIFE OF ONE OF HIS BROTHERS, WAS EXPECTING A BABY AT THE TIME.

PRINCESS! I FEAR FOR THE LIFE OF THE UNBORN CHILD.

DO YOU SUGGEST THAT I RUN AWAY FROM HERE? BUT WHERE CAN I GO?

I CAN SHOW YOU A SECRET DOOR. YOU CAN ESCAPE INTO THE WOODS.

ESCAPING FROM THE PALACE, SUMANADEVI WANDERED IN THE FOREST.

AN OLD MAN, WHO WAS PASSING BY, TOOK PITY ON HER.

IF YOU COME WITH ME TO MY VILLAGE, I WILL ARRANGE FOR YOUR STAY.

SHE ACCOMPANIED HIM. WHILE THEY WERE ON THEIR WAY—

NO! I CANNOT WALK ANY FARTHER.

DON'T WORRY, DAUGHTER! MY HOME IS CLOSE BY. I'LL FETCH MY WIFE. YOU REST UNDER THIS NIGRODHA TREE.

IT WAS UNDER THAT NIGRODHA TREE THAT A BOY WAS BORN TO SUMANADEVI.

LET'S CALL HIM, NIGRODHA KUMAR.

NIGRODHA KUMAR GREW UP IN THAT VILLAGE AND BECAME A MONK AT A VERY TENDER AGE.

MEANWHILE, ASHOKA HAD BECOME A POWERFUL KING. AT HIS COURT —

MINISTER, IS MY KINGDOM PEACEFUL? ARE THE BORDERS QUIET?

YES, YOUR MAJESTY. EVEN TAXILA AND UJJAINI ARE QUIET.

STILL WE SHOULD NOT REST TILL KALINGA IS CONQUERED.

WHY YOUR MAJESTY?

IT IS INDEPENDENT TODAY AND MAY RAISE ITS HEAD ANY MOMENT.

WAR IT WILL HAVE TO BE.

COMMANDER! PREPARE FOR THE BATTLE.

ASHOKA'S ARMY INVADED KALINGA.

THE SOLDIERS OF KALINGA FOUGHT BRAVELY.

AT LAST—

WE HAVE WON. KALINGA IS OURS.

I SHALL VISIT KALINGA.

HE SAW THE SUFFERINGS OF THE PEOPLE.

OH! NO!

LET'S RETURN.

IN THE PALACE—

YOUR MAJESTY! AREN'T YOU WELL?

I HAVE LOST MY PEACE OF MIND.

TO ADD TO HIS GRIEF A MESSENGER CAME FROM VIDISHA-NAGAR.

YOUR MAJESTY! I HAVE BROUGHT THIS LETTER FROM VIDISHA DEVI.

Arya putra, you have broken the promise. I am sending the children to you. Please look after them properly.

Yours

WHERE IS VIDISHA?

SHE PLANS TO JOIN THE SANGHA OF BUDDHA.

ASHOKA DREW SOME COMFORT FROM THE PRESENCE OF HIS CHILDREN. BUT HE CONTINUED TO BROOD OVER THE KILLINGS.

ONE DAY, FROM HIS PALACE WINDOW, HE SAW A MONK PASSING ALONG THE ROAD.

WHO CAN THIS BE? WHY DO I FEEL DRAWN TOWARDS HIM?

24

A TRANSFORMATION CAME ABOUT IN ASHOKA. ALL HIS ATTENTION NOW WAS ON BRINGING PEACE AND HAPPINESS TO THE PEOPLE.

FOR THE COMFORT OF TRAVELLERS, EVEN IN THE WOODS, HE BUILT REST HOUSES AND DISPENSARIES.

HE ERECTED PILLARS...

...AND CARVED INSTRUCTIONS ON ROCKS.

PRIYADARSHI, THE BELOVED KING OF GOD SAYS THIS ...

ONE DAY—

I HAVE GIVEN AWAY ALL THINGS DEAR TO ME.

EXCEPT...

EXCEPT WHAT, MAHINDRA?

YOUR CHILDREN.

YOUR SON WISHES TO JOIN THE SANGHA.

MUST YOU, MAHINDRA? IT IS WITH A HEAVY HEART— BUT I GIVE YOU PERMISSION.

FATHER, ALLOW ME TO JOIN THE NUNNERY.

OH! SANGHAMITRA!!

MY HUSBAND AND SON HAVE RENOUNCED THE WORLD. I TAKE NO PLEASURE IN LIFE.

YOU MAY JOIN THE NUNNERY.

AFTER A FEW YEARS—

FATHER, I WOULD LIKE TO GO TO LANKA.

GO, MY SON. GO WITH MY BLESSINGS.

TWO YEARS LATER—

FATHER, I HAVE COME TO BID YOU GOOD-BYE.

WHAT DO YOU MEAN, SANGHA-MITRA?

A MESSAGE HAS BEEN RECEIVED FROM LANKA. THEY NEED NUNS AT THE MISSION.

HM...

DO NOT GRIEVE.

BY SACRIFICING YOUR DEAR ONES YOU HAVE PROVED THAT DHARMA IS DEAR TO YOU. YOU ARE INDEED, DHARMASHOKA.

THUS ASHOKA BECAME DHARMASHOKA. HE RULED FOR MANY YEARS AND LOOKED AFTER THE WELFARE OF THE SUBJECTS OF HIS VAST EMPIRE AS A FATHER WOULD LOOK AFTER HIS CHILDREN.

THE FIVE PRINCIPLES OF CO-EXISTENCE, WHICH HE PROPA-GATED, ARE STILL RESPECTED THE WORLD OVER. THE ASHOKA PILLAR AT SARNATH REMINDS US EVEN TILL THIS DAY OF HIS GREATNESS. THE 'DHARMA CHAKRA' ON THE ASHOKA PILLAR ADORNS OUR NATIONAL FLAG.

CHANDRAGUPTA MAURYA
THE DETERMINED PRINCE

The route to your roots

CHANDRAGUPTA MAURYA

Chandragupta Maurya defeated the Nandas and established himself on the throne of Magadha in 321 B.C. It was a journey fraught with dangerous challenges but his chance meeting with the wily Chanakya changed his destiny forever. The clever Brahmin showed him how by the sheer brilliance of his wit and wile he could help the young Mauryan prince to rise from being an unknown warrior to one of the greatest emperors of India.

Script
Subba Rao

Illustrations
Ram Waeerkar

Editor
Anant Pai

Cover illustration by: P.G.Sirur

CHANDRAGUPTA MAURYA

CROWN PRINCE NANDA WAS THE VIRTUAL RULER OF MAGADHA BECAUSE SARVARTHA SIDDHI, ITS AGED KING, LED A RETIRED LIFE. THE CROWN PRINCE AND HIS EIGHT BROTHERS WERE TOGETHER KNOWN AS THE NANDAS.

THAT WAS THE BEST HUNT WE'VE EVER HAD.

ONLY BECAUSE WE DIDN'T INVITE OUR COUSIN, MAURYA, AND HIS HUNDRED SONS TO JOIN US!

NOT THAT NANDA DIDN'T KNOW IT!

WHAT YOU SAY IS TRUE. WHEN THE MAURYAS ARE AROUND, THERE'S NOT AN ANIMAL LEFT FOR US TO SHOOT!

THE MAURYAS ARE POWERFUL, INTELLIGENT AND POPULAR. ONE DAY THEY WILL PROVE A THREAT TO US.

IF WE LET THEM LIVE LONG ENOUGH TO DO SO!

YOU MEAN, YOU WON'T ALLOW THEM TO... BUT HOW?

I HAVE MY PLANS. BUT I'M BIDING MY TIME.

A FEW MONTHS LATER, NANDA STOOD GAZING AT A SPECIALLY CONSTRUCTED PALACE OUTSIDE PATALIPUTRA, THE CAPITAL.

NOW I'M READY FOR THEM. THE OLD KING WILL SOON BE GOING AWAY ON A PILGRIMAGE. THEN SHALL I STRIKE!

AS SOON AS SARVARTHA SIDDHI WENT ON HIS PILGRIMAGE, NANDA CALLED ON MAURYA.

MAURYA, I'VE ARRANGED FOR A BIG HUNT IN THE FOREST TOMORROW. I WANT YOU AND YOUR VALIANT SONS TO JOIN US.

WE'D BE ONLY TOO GLAD TO ACCEPT YOUR INVITATION.

OF ALL THE COURTIERS, NOBLES AND PRINCES WHO HAD JOINED THE PARTY, CHANDRAGUPTA, THE YOUNGEST OF THE MAURYAS, WAS AS USUAL EASILY THE BEST SHOT.

AFTER THE HUNT, WHEN NANDA BROUGHT HIS GUESTS TO THE NEWLY BUILT PALACE FOR DINNER, HE TURNED TO MAURYA.

THIS HAS BEEN SPECIALLY BUILT...

....FOR US?

YES.

FOR YOUR LAST SUPPER. I TRUST MY MEN HAVE MADE THE NECESSARY ARRANGE- MENTS.

AS SOON AS EVERYONE HAD ENTERED THE PALACE, NANDA CALLED MAURYA ASIDE.

I'VE JUST LEARNT THAT ALL OF US CANNOT EAT IN THE MAIN HALL. SOME WILL HAVE TO BE SERVED IN THE CELLAR. WHAT AN EMBARRASSING SITUATION!

DON'T WORRY. I'LL EAT WITH MY SONS IN THE CELLAR. OUR GUESTS SHOULD BE SERVED IN THE MAIN HALL.

MAURYA SPOKE TO HIS SONS AND THEY TROOPED INTO THE CELLAR.

SO FAR SO GOOD. HE DOESN'T SUSPECT A THING.

IN THE CELLAR, THE NANDAS MOVED ABOUT PRETENDING TO LEAD THEM TO THEIR SEATS. THEN—

NOW TO SLOWLY MAKE OUR WAY OUT OF THE CELLAR.

AS SOON AS THE NANDAS WERE OUT OF THE CELLAR—

BANG!

WHAT WAS THAT?

CHANDRAGUPTA RAN TOWARDS THE DOOR.

IT'S THE DOOR! OPEN THE DOOR!

YOU WILL NEVER COME OUT OF THIS PALACE ALIVE.

FATHER, WE HAVE BEEN TRICKED BY THE NANDAS AND THEIR HENCHMEN!

WHILE THE NANDAS AND THE NOBLES MADE FOR THE CAPITAL, THE MAURYAS STRUGGLED IN VAIN TO BREAK OPEN THE DOOR. DAYS PASSED BY.

WE ARE DOOMED.

ONE BY ONE THE MAURYAS BEGAN TO DIE OF STARVATION.

EVEN IF ONE OF US SURVIVES, HE SHALL TAKE REVENGE!

WITHOUT A DOUBT, FATHER!

A FEW DAYS LATER, THE GUARDS REPORTED TO NANDA.

YOUR MAJESTY, ALL THE PRISONERS EXCEPT ONE HAVE DIED. THE PLACE IS REEKING.

THE STENCH MAY ATTRACT ATTENTION.

AND ONE MAURYA CAN'T DO US MUCH HARM.

TRANSFER THE LONE PRISONER TO THE STATE PRISON AND BURN DOWN THE PALACE.

THE ORDER WAS CARRIED OUT. CHANDRAGUPTA, THE LONE SURVIVOR WAS LED AWAY TO THE STATE PRISON.

FATHER! BROTHERS! REST IN PEACE. I WILL AVENGE YOUR DEATH.

MEANWHILE, THE NEWS OF THE DEATH OF THE MIGHTY MAURYAS HAD SPREAD FAR AND WIDE. KING PARVATAK OF PARVATA DESH WAS JUBILANT. HE SENT FOR HIS COUNCIL OF MINISTERS.

NOW THAT THE MIGHTY MAURYAS ARE NO MORE, THE WAY IS CLEAR FOR US TO MARCH INTO MAGADHA.

MY LORD, SHOULDN'T WE FIRST MAKE SURE THAT THE MAURYAS ARE REALLY DEAD?

YOU ARE RIGHT.

KAMALAPIDA SHALL GO TO PATALIPUTRA AND CREATE A SITUATION WHICH WILL COMPEL THE MAURYAS, IF ALIVE, TO COME OUT OF HIDING.

KAMALAPIDA, PARVATAK'S TRUSTED SPY, CAME TO PATALIPUTRA, BRINGING WITH HIM A LION IN A CAGE.

I CHALLENGE THE MEN OF MAGADHA TO SET THE LION FREE WITHOUT BREAKING OPEN THE CAGE.

THE PEOPLE OF PATALIPUTRA FLOCKED ROUND THE CAGE.

BUT THIS CAGE HAS NO DOOR!

HOW DID THE LION GET IN?

THE LION WAS BORN WITH THE CAGE AROUND IT.

HA! HA!

IMPOSSIBLE!

THEN HOW COULD IT ENTER THE CAGE WHICH HAS NO DOOR?

WHAT! ISN'T THERE A SINGLE ONE AMONG YOU WHO CAN SOLVE THE MYSTERY?

THE MATTER WAS REPORTED TO NANDA.

IT'S A SHAME THAT NO ONE HAS BEEN ABLE TO SOLVE THE MYSTERY. WHERE ARE THE WISE MEN OF PATALIPUTRA?

NANDA HAD A HERALD SENT ROUND THE CAPITAL.

GIVE EAR... ANYONE WHO CAN SOLVE THE MYSTERY OF THE LION AND UPHOLD THE HONOUR OF MAGADHA WILL BE REWARDED.

THE FOLLOWING MORNING, THE HERALD STOOD BEFORE NANDA.

YOUR MAJESTY, ONLY ONE MAN IS PREPARED TO ACCEPT THE CHALLENGE. BUT HE IS A PRISONER.

SO WHAT? SET HIM FREE AND TAKE HIM TO THE VISITOR.

THE PRISONER WHO WAS NONE OTHER THAN CHANDRAGUPTA WAS TAKEN TO KAMALAPIDA.

WHERE DO YOU COME FROM?

HE MUST BE FROM PARVATA DESH.

I HAVE NO HOME. I LIVE IN CAVES, ON THE HILLS.

9

CHANDRAGUPTA HAD A GOOD LOOK AT THE LION.

WHEN THE GUARD BRANDISHES THE STAFF, THE LION JUMPS IN RAGE. STILL...

CHANDRAGUPTA HAD A BLINDFOLDED ELEPHANT BROUGHT AND PARADED BEFORE THE LION.

STRANGE! THE LION DOES NOT REACT. COULD IT BE A FAKE ONE?

NEXT, CHANDRAGUPTA HAD SOME MEAT BROUGHT FROM THE PALACE KITCHEN WHICH HE OFFERED TO THE LION.

WHY DOESN'T THE LION REACH FOR THE MEAT?

IT IS TRAINED NOT TO ACCEPT FOOD FROM STRANGERS. LET ME OFFER THE MEAT.

WHEN THE GUARD OFFERED THE MEAT, THE LION RUSHED FORWARD.

SEE?

INDEED I DO!

ALL RIGHT. NOW PLEASE HAND OVER THE STAFF TO ME AND THEN OFFER THE MEAT TO THE LION!

WHEN THE FIRE DIED DOWN—

YOUR MAJESTY! LOOK! THE IRON SKELETON OF THE LION! AS THE VISITOR WAVED THE MAGNETIZED STAFF. THE FAKE LION MOVED.

WHERE IS THAT VISITOR?

HE COULD NOT BE SEEN ANYWHERE.

NANDA TURNED TO CHANDRAGUPTA.

YOU HAVE SAVED THE HONOUR OF MAGADHA. WE ARE PLEASED TO RELEASE YOU FROM PRISON AND PLACE YOU IN CHARGE OF THE STATE GUEST-HOUSE.

I AM GRATEFUL TO YOU, YOUR MAJESTY.

LATER, NANDA EXPLAINED HIS MOVE TO HIS BROTHERS.

BEING A PRINCE, CHANDRAGUPTA WILL BE INDIFFERENT TO THE COMFORTS OF THE VISITORS IN THE GUEST-HOUSE. AN ENRAGED BRAHMAN MAY CURSE HIM, AND BRING ABOUT HIS DESTRUCTION.

LET US HOPE SO.

BUT NANDA WAS WRONG. CHANDRAGUPTA TOOK GOOD CARE OF HIS GUESTS. ONE AFTERNOON, HE SAW A BRAHMAN APPROACHING THE GUEST-HOUSE.

SUDDENLY, THE BRAHMAN STOPPED.

THIS GRASS HURTS ME.

HE SAT DOWN TO PULL OUT THE GRASS...

...AND RESUMED HIS JOURNEY ONLY AFTER HE HAD UPROOTED ALL THE GRASS IN HIS PATH.

HE SEEMS TO BE A MAN OF DETERMINATION. HIS SUPPORT WOULD BE OF GREAT HELP TO ME.

HE RAN UP TO THE **BRAHMAN**.

REVERED ONE, PLEASE HAVE DINNER AT THE GUEST-HOUSE BEFORE YOU PROCEED.

IT IS VERY KIND OF YOU TO INVITE ME.

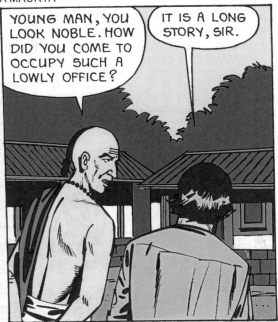

YOUNG MAN, YOU LOOK NOBLE. HOW DID YOU COME TO OCCUPY SUCH A LOWLY OFFICE?

IT IS A LONG STORY, SIR.

WHEN CHANDRAGUPTA TOLD HIM ALL—

DON'T WORRY, CHANDRAGUPTA. I, CHANAKYA, WILL HELP YOU AVENGE THE DEATH OF YOUR FATHER AND BROTHERS.

AT THE GUEST-HOUSE, CHANDRAGUPTA OFFERED A SEAT OF HONOUR TO CHANAKYA AND SERVED HIM PERSONALLY.

JUST THEN, THE NANDAS, WHO WERE RETURNING HOME AFTER A HUNT, HAPPENED TO COME THERE.

WHAT IMPUDENCE! A MAN IN RAGS OCCUPYING THE SEAT OF HONOUR! GET UP, YOU SCAMP!

CHANAKYA IGNORED THEM AND CONTINUED TO EAT.

DID YOU NOT HEAR US? HOW DARE YOU IGNORE US, YOU KNAVE!

WHEN NANDA PULLED HIM UP, CHANAKYA'S KNOTTED HAIR CAME LOOSE.

YOU REPROBATES! I WILL NOT TIE UP MY HAIR UNTIL YOU ARE DESTROYED! IF I FAIL, MY NAME IS NOT CHANAKYA.

AS CHANAKYA WALKED OUT, SEETHING WITH ANGER—

HA! HA! MIGHTY WORDS INDEED, FROM ONE SO PUNY!

THAT NIGHT, CHANDRAGUPTA SLIPPED OUT OF THE GUEST-HOUSE AND MET CHANAKYA.

BEFORE WE PLAN OUR MOVES, I MUST KNOW WHO ARE NANDA'S FRIENDS AND WHO HIS FOES.

THE KING OF KASHI IS A STAUNCH FRIEND. PARVATAK IS HIS ENEMY.

THEN LET US GO TO KING PARVATAK AND ENLIST HIS SUPPORT.

WHEN THEY CALLED ON PARVATAK AT HIS CAPITAL, THEY RECEIVED A WARM WELCOME.

WHAT CAN I DO FOR YOU, O REVERED CHANAKYA?

WE WANT YOUR SUPPORT TO VANQUISH THE WICKED NANDA AND HIS BROTHERS.

I WISH I COULD HELP YOU. BUT I AM FACING A THREAT FROM THE KING OF LAMPAKA.

IF THE THREAT FROM LAMPAKA IS TAKEN CARE OF?

THEN MY ARMY WILL BE AT THE DISPOSAL OF CHANDRAGUPTA.

IF THE KING OF LAMPAKA IS HIMSELF THREATENED WITH AGGRESSION, HE WOULD NOT BE IN A POSITION TO SEND HIS ARMY AGAINST YOU.

LET US SET THE KING OF KAMARUPA AGAINST HIM. SEND AN INTELLIGENT SPY TO THE KING OF KAMARUPA. LET HIM SEE ME BEFORE HE LEAVES.

I WILL SEND KAMALAPIDA.

INSTRUCTED BY CHANAKYA, KAMALAPIDA AND HIS COMPANION LEFT FOR THE KINGDOM OF KAMARUPA. WHEN THEY REACHED THE GARDEN AT THE OUTSKIRTS OF THE CAPITAL—

WAIT HERE, AND COME TO THE ROYAL COURT AFTER SOME TIME. AND DON'T FORGET CHANAKYA'S INSTRUCTIONS.

I WON'T, KAMALAPIDA.

KAMALAPIDA SOON REACHED THE COURT OF THE KING OF KAMARUPA.

YOUR MAJESTY, I'VE BROUGHT A PROPOSAL FROM OUR KING, PARVATAK. HE REQUESTS YOU TO GIVE YOUR PRINCESS IN MARRIAGE TO OUR PRINCE, MALAYAKETU.

WE ARE DELIGHTED TO RECEIVE THIS PROPOSAL. WE WILL...

JUST THEN, KAMALAPIDA'S COMPANION ENTERED.

EXCUSE ME, YOUR MAJESTY. I HAVE AN URGENT MESSAGE FOR KAMALAPIDA, THE ENVOY OF KING PARVATAK.

WHEN KAMALAPIDA *READ* THE MESSAGE, HE TURNED PALE.

WHAT'S THE MATTER? NO BAD NEWS, I HOPE.

YOUR MAJESTY, IT IS ABOUT THE MARRIAGE PROPOSAL. HE WANTS...NO! I CAN'T. PARDON ME.

OVERCOME BY CURIOSITY, THE KING ORDERED HIS MINISTER TO TAKE THE LETTER FROM KAMALAPIDA AND READ IT ALOUD.

...IT IS REPORTED THAT THE KING OF LAMPAKA OPENLY CALLED THE LORD OF KAMARUPA A MAN OF LOW ORIGIN SINCE ONE OF HIS ANCESTORS HAD MARRIED A COMMONER...

...I HOLD THE LORD OF KAMARUPA IN HIGH ESTEEM; AND YET, IN THE LIGHT OF THE REMARKS MADE BY THE KING OF LAMPAKA...

ENOUGH! THAT WRETCH WILL PAY FOR HIS MALICIOUS AND DEFAMATORY REMARKS.

THEN HE TURNED TO KAMALAPIDA.

GO BACK TO YOUR LORD AND TELL HIM THAT I WILL RESPOND TO HIS PROPOSAL ONLY AFTER THE KING OF LAMPAKA IS VANQUISHED.

AS KAMALAPIDA AND HIS COMPANION LEFT FOR THEIR KINGDOM, THEY SAW KAMARUPA'S ARMY MARCHING TOWARDS THE KINGDOM OF LAMPAKA.

CHANAKYA'S PLAN HAS SUCCEEDED! THE KING OF LAMPAKA WILL BE KEPT BUSY.

WHEN PARVATAK HEARD THE NEWS, HE WAS JUBILANT.

CHANAKYA HAS GOT RID OF MY ENEMIES WITHOUT RESORTING TO ARMS.

YOUR MAJESTY, CHANAKYA CAN BRING ABOUT THE FALL OF NANDA IN A SIMILAR WAY.

YES. HE NEED NOT DEPEND UPON US. HE HAS ASKED FOR OUR HELP ONLY TO HONOUR US.

LATER, WHEN CHANDRAGUPTA AND CHANAKYA CALLED ON HIM—

HOLY ONE, MY ARMY IS AT THE DISPOSAL OF CHANDRAGUPTA.

I AM GRATEFUL TO YOU, YOUR MAJESTY.

NOW WE MUST SEND ENVOYS TO VARIOUS KINGDOMS, SOLICITING THEIR ASSISTANCE.

I WILL DO SO IMMEDIATELY.

SEND KAMALAPIDA TO KASHI.

TO KASHI? BUT THE KING OF KASHI IS A CLOSE FRIEND OF NANDA. HE WON'T HELP US.

PLEASE DO AS I SAY.

AS YOU WISH.

MEANWHILE, NANDA HAD COME TO KNOW OF THE IMPENDING ATTACK BY CHANDRAGUPTA.

HOW UNGRATEFUL HE IS! WE SET HIM FREE AND HE TURNS AGAINST US.

HE WILL REPENT, YOUR MAJESTY.

JUST THEN, A GUARD ENTERED.

YOUR MAJESTY, AN ENVOY FROM KASHI AWAITS YOUR PLEASURE.

BRING HIM IN.

THE ENVOY ENTERED AND BOWED TO NANDA.

YOUR MAJESTY, CHANDRA-GUPTA AND PARVATAK HAVE SOLICITED OUR HELP IN THEIR WAR AGAINST YOU.

DON'T THEY KNOW YOUR KING IS A TRUSTED FRIEND OF OURS?

OBVIOUSLY THEY DON'T, YOUR MAJESTY. THAT'S WHY OUR KING WANTS TO KNOW WHETHER YOU COULD USE THEIR IGNORANCE TO YOUR ADVANTAGE.

COULD WE, RAKSHASA?

RAKSHASA, THE PRIME MINISTER, WAS THOUGHTFUL FOR A MOMENT. THEN—

LET YOUR KING PRETEND FRIENDSHIP WITH CHANDRAGUPTA AND JOIN HIM WITH HIS ARMY...

...AND WHEN A SUITABLE OPPORTUNITY PRESENTS ITSELF, LET HIM EITHER KILL CHANDRAGUPTA OR CAPTURE HIM OR PARVATAK'S SON, MALAYAKETU.

A GOOD IDEA!

I WILL CONVEY YOUR MESSAGE TO OUR KING.

AND THE ENVOY LEFT FOR KASHI.

BRIEFED BY RAKSHASA, THE KING OF KASHI SENT FOR KAMALAPIDA.

AFTER GIVING THE MATTER DUE THOUGHT, WE HAVE DECIDED TO SIDE WITH CHANDRAGUPTA. OUR ARMY WILL LEAVE IMMEDIATELY.

CHANAKYA'S PREDICTION HAS COME TRUE.

NOT IMMEDIATELY, YOUR MAJESTY. CHANDRAGUPTA OR MALAYAKETU WILL COME AND TAKE YOU TO PATALIPUTRA. TILL THEN, PLEASE WAIT.

AND YOU'LL HAVE TO WAIT IN VAIN. CHANAKYA IS BRILLIANT.

YES. I'LL WAIT —WAIT FOR THEM TO WALK INTO MY TRAP.

EVERY DAY HE WOULD QUESTION KAMALAPIDA.

WHEN IS CHANDRA-GUPTA COMING? OR WILL IT BE MALAYAKETU?

ONE OF THEM SHOULD BE HERE ANY MOMENT, YOUR MAJESTY. I DON'T KNOW WHAT'S KEEPING THEM.

WHILE THE KING OF KASHI WAITED, CHANDRAGUPTA'S ARMY MARCHED TO PATALIPUTRA.

NANDA AND HIS BROTHERS LEFT FOR THE BATTLE-FIELD. ON THE WAY—

ISN'T THAT THE YAGNA* RAKSHASA HAS ARRANGED FOR OUR VICTORY?

NANDA PAID HIS RESPECTS TO SAGE MASOPAVASI WHO WAS CONDUCTING THE YAGNA.

TOMORROW, WHEN THE FINAL OFFERING IS MADE, A DIVINE HAND WILL EMERGE FROM THE SACRIFICIAL FIRE TO RECEIVE IT...

...AND WITHIN MINUTES THE ENEMY SOLDIERS WILL COLLAPSE AND DIE IN THOUSANDS.

* FIRE-SACRIFICE

NANDA WAS DEEPLY IMPRESSED.

HOLY ONE, COULD WE COME AND WITNESS THE FINAL OFFERING?

YOU ARE WELCOME.

NANDA AND HIS BROTHERS TOOK LEAVE OF THE SAGE AND WENT THEIR WAY.

IN THE BATTLE THAT FOLLOWED, CHANDRAGUPTA'S FORCES HAD AN EDGE OVER THE ENEMY.

TURN BACK!

CHANDRAGUPTA IS AFTER US.

WHEN DEFEAT FOR NANDA WAS IMMINENT, RAKSHASA FOUGHT DESPERATELY AND TURNED THE TIDE IN FAVOUR OF NANDA.

AT THE END OF THE DAY'S BATTLE—

BUT FOR YOUR COURAGE, RAKSHASA, WE WOULD HAVE BEEN DEFEATED. WE ARE INDEBTED TO YOU.

I ONLY DID MY DUTY.

OUR ALLY, THE KING OF KASHI, WILL BE DELIVERING CHANDRAGUPTA TO US ANY MOMENT.

WE ARE SURE THAT YOUR PLAN WILL WORK.

THAT NIGHT, NANDA SLEPT PEACEFULLY.

AT MIDNIGHT, HE WAS WOKEN UP BY THE DISCIPLES OF MASOPAVASI.

THE FINAL OFFERING WILL BE MADE SHORTLY.

WE'LL START IMMEDIATELY.

NANDA AND HIS BROTHERS LEFT FOR THE SACRIFICIAL SITE. WHEN THEY REACHED THE PLACE—

YOUR MAJESTY, THE KING OF KASHI HAS CAPTURED MALAYAKETU AND HAS SENT HIM HERE UNDER ARMED ESCORT. SHALL WE OPEN THE GATE OF THE FORT TO ADMIT THEM?

WITHOUT A MOMENT'S DELAY!

AFTER SOME TIME—

VICTORY TO THE NANDAS! VICTORY TO THE KING OF KASHI.

AH! HERE COMES MALAYAKETU.

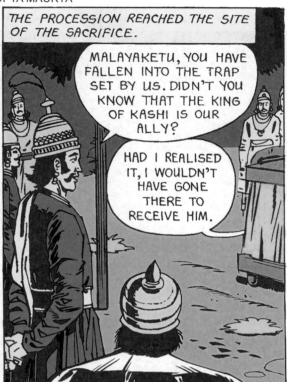

THE PROCESSION REACHED THE SITE OF THE SACRIFICE.

MALAYAKETU, YOU HAVE FALLEN INTO THE TRAP SET BY US. DIDN'T YOU KNOW THAT THE KING OF KASHI IS OUR ALLY?

HAD I REALISED IT, I WOULDN'T HAVE GONE THERE TO RECEIVE HIM.

MALAYAKETU, YOUR FATHER LOVES YOU DEARLY. WE'LL RELEASE YOU ONLY WHEN HE SURRENDERS CHANDRAGUPTA TO US.

HE WILL NEVER DO IT.

HE WILL. WHY DON'T YOU COME OUT OF THE PALANQUIN AND SPEAK? ARE YOU SHY?

THE NEXT MOMENT—

IT IS NOT MALAYAKETU. WE'VE BEEN DUPED!

THE SOLDIERS WHO HAD BROUGHT THE FAKE MALAYAKETU, FELL UPON NANDA AND HIS MEN.

THESE ARE CHANDRAGUPTA'S SOLDIERS IN DISGUISE! OH, GOD!

JUST THEN, MASOPAVASI WHO WAS NONE OTHER THAN CHANAKYA'S OWN MAN, SET FIRE TO THE SACRIFICIAL SITE.

YES. THE TIME FOR THE FINAL OFFERING— THE HEADS OF THE NANDAS — HAS ARRIVED.

THEN CHANDRAGUPTA APPEARED ON THE SCENE. IN THE BATTLE THAT FOLLOWED HE OVERCAME NANDA.

THE MURDERS OF MY FATHER AND BROTHERS SHALL SOON BE AVENGED!

THE REST OF THE NANDAS WERE KILLED IN THE BATTLE.

HOLY ONE! I BOW TO YOU. YOU'VE MADE THIS VICTORY POSSIBLE. I AWAIT YOUR COMMAND.

CHANDRAGUPTA! BE A JUST KING AND STRIVE FOR THE WELFARE OF THE PEOPLE. MAKE THE COUNTRY STRONG AND UNITED.

AND CHANAKYA TIED UP HIS TUFT. IT WAS DAWN BY THEN. CHANDRAGUPTA ENTERED PATALIPUTRA IN TRIUMPH.

VICTORY TO CHANDRAGUPTA!

WELCOME HOME, CHANDRAGUPTA!

SAMUDRA GUPTA

THE LUTE-PLAYING CONQUEROR

The route to your roots

SAMUDRA GUPTA

Can a music-loving, scholarly prince be a successful king? Will a skilled and com-
mitted warrior encourage the arts and science? Samudra Gupta proved he was a
multi-faceted ruler. By bringing peace to a huge area of the warring subcontinent,
this benevolent king gave his people the leisure to be creative. His court official
Harishena engraved his master's achievement on the Ashoka pillar in Allahabad.

Script	Illustrations	Editor
Kamala Chandrakant	Souren Roy	Anant Pai

Cover illustration by: Ramesh Umrotkar

SAMUDRA GUPTA

THE EARLY DECADES OF THE FOURTH CENTURY: THE SONS OF THE KING AND THE MINISTERS OF ANCIENT MAGADHA WERE LISTENING WITH RAPT ATTENTION TO THEIR GURU WHEN...

...CHANDRA GUPTA, THE KING OF MAGADHA, SILENTLY RODE UP, DISMOUNTED...

...AND HID HIMSELF BEHIND A BUSH.

YOU MAY NOW CHOOSE YOUR WEAPONS AND YOUR OPPONENTS.

THE KING OBSERVED HIS ELDEST SON, KACHA, WITH PRIDE.

SURELY, NONE CAN WIELD THE SWORD AS DEFTLY AS HE DOES!

BUT AS KACHA WARMED UP...

...CHANDRA GUPTA GREW ALARMED.

HE'S LOST CONTROL OF HIMSELF! HE'LL KILL HARISHENA!

THE GURU HOWEVER WAS ALERT.

KACHA!

2

THAT'S IT! THAT WAS EXCELLENT!

SUDDENLY SAMUDRA GUPTA FLUNG HIS AXE ASIDE ...

...AND EMBRACED HIS OPPONENT.

SOON —

WELL DONE, MY SON. I AM PROUD OF YOUR SKILL ... YOUR SELF-CONTROL ... AND MOST OF ALL ...

MAHARAJ!

FATHER!

...I AM PROUD OF THE WAY YOU TREATED YOUR LOSING OPPONENT!

LATER, AS THEY WALKED TOWARDS THE HALL WHERE MUSIC WAS TAUGHT —

WHY MUST A KSHATRIYA FIGHT?

FOR FAME! FOR GLORY!

A KSHATRIYA WHO FIGHTS FOR PERSONAL GLORY ONLY BRINGS MISERY IN HIS WAKE.

BLOODSHED, DESTRUCTION, POVERTY, INSECURITY... THESE FOLLOW WANTON WARFARE.

HA! HA! HA! FINE-SOUNDING WORDS, BUT ABSOLUTELY SENSELESS.

SAMUDRA GUPTA, DO YOU REALLY BELIEVE THAT A KSHATRIYA MUST NOT FIGHT?

OH, HE MUST! BUT NOT FOR PERSONAL GLORY.

HE MUST FIGHT FOR ORDER... FOR STABILITY. HE MUST FIGHT TO UPHOLD DHARMA... LIKE THE PANDAVAS.

THE PANDAVAS, HE SAYS. WHAT A FINE EXAMPLE! KSHATRIYAS WHO FOUGHT DRONA AND BHEESHMA, THEIR GURUS!

WHOM THEY DEEPLY RESPECT-ED, LET ME REMIND YOU.

BUT DRONA AND BHEESHMA HAD TO BE FOUGHT AS THEY WERE IN THE ENEMY CAMP.

AN ENEMY CAMP OF BLOOD RELATIVES! PAH! GIVE UP, SAMUDRA GUPTA.

THE ONLY RELATIVE A KSHATRIYA HAS IS DHARMA.

AND HE MUST BE PREPARED TO FIGHT EVEN HIS OWN BROTHER IN DEFENCE OF DHARMA.

VERY TRUE, MY SON.

MAHARAJ!

HE IS RIGHT, KACHA. ONLY THOSE WHO ARE CAPABLE OF PROTECTING DHARMA CAN CLAIM THE RIGHT TO KINGSHIP. AND THE KAURAVAS HAD BY THEIR IGNOBLE ACTIONS LOST THAT RIGHT.

INSIDE THE MUSIC HALL —

IN THIS DISCIPLINE SAMUDRA GUPTA EXCELS ALL. HARISHENA IS GOOD AT COMPOSING VERSES BUT SAMUDRA GUPTA OUTSHINES HIM IN RENDERING THEM.

HARISHENA, HAVE YOU COMPOSED THE VERSES?

YES, SIR.

HARISHENA RECITED THE LYRIC, THE GURU COMPOSED THE MUSIC AND —

ALL RIGHT. LET'S BEGIN. SA-A-A-A

WHEN I BECOME KING, I WILL SPARE MY SONS THIS SILLY ROUTINE.

KACHA DID NOT KNOW THAT HE WAS BEING OBSERVED.

THEY WILL LEARN TO FIGHT AND CONQUER... NOT INDULGE IN SUCH FUTILE PURSUITS.

SIR, I...I WOULD LIKE TO PLAY A PIECE THAT WAS NOT TAUGHT HERE. I WANT TO KNOW WHAT YOU THINK OF IT.

PLAY IT SON, BY ALL MEANS DO!

WHEN THE PIECE WAS OVER —

DELIGHTFUL! WHO COMPOSED THE LYRIC? WHO SET THE MUSIC?

MY EFFORT, SIR. BOTH, THE LYRIC AND THE MUSIC.

WHY, YOU HAVE PUT TO SHAME BOTH TUMBURU AND NARADA!

YOU SHOULD HAVE BEEN THE SON OF A POET OR A MUSICIAN...

...NOT A KING!

PERHAPS, YES. FOR...

...WITHOUT MUSIC, MY SOUL, THE SOUL OF A PEOPLE WOULD PERISH.

THEN WHY DO YOU PRACTISE THE MILITARY ARTS?

BECAUSE THE BEAUTIFUL PURSUITS OF PEACE CAN FLOURISH ONLY WHEN A KINGDOM IS FREE FROM WARS AND WANT.

AND AS THE SON OF A KING ONE OF MY DUTIES IS TO HELP THE KING IN ENSURING PEACE FOR THE FINER PURSUITS.

NONSENSE!

THE TRUE KING DOES NOT STOP FIGHTING AND ANNEXING TERRITORIES FOR GREATER POWER.

MAHARAJ, AS YOUR ELDEST SON AND HEIR TO THE THRONE MY HANDS ARE MEANT TO WIELD THE SWORD...NOT PLAY THE LUTE!

HM-M-M!

THE BOYS ARE FEARLESS, STRONG AND INTELLIGENT.

AND YET EACH ONE IS SO DIFFERENT...

CHANDRA GUPTA THEN LEFT FOR HIS PALACE.

THERE, KUMARADEVI, THE LICHCHAVI PRINCESS WHO WAS HIS FAVOURITE QUEEN AND THE MOTHER OF SAMUDRA GUPTA, WELCOMED HIM WITH A SMILE.

HAVE YOU FOUND THE ANSWER TO YOUR QUESTION?

YES. I THINK I HAVE.

BUT WHY DID YOU WANT TO KNOW WHICH OF YOUR SONS WAS THE BEST?

BECAUSE HE...

... IS GOING TO BE MY SUCCESSOR!

I...I DON'T UNDERSTAND.

ACCORDING TO TRADITION, YOUR ELDEST SON IS YOUR SUCCESSOR.

YE-ES. BUT...

...TRADITION WILL HAVE TO BE WAIVED IN THIS CASE.

OH!

11

WHEN IT WAS TIME FOR HIS SONS TO GET MARRIED, CHANDRA GUPTA RESERVED THE MOST ACCOMPLISHED BRIDE FOR SAMUDRA GUPTA.

SHOULDN'T THE BEST ALLIANCE GO TO YOUR ELDEST SON?

NO. SAMUDRA GUPTA WILL MARRY DATTADEVI AND FOR VERY GOOD REASONS.

AND SO SAMUDRA GUPTA WAS MARRIED TO DATTADEVI +

ONE DAY WHILE CHANDRA GUPTA, HIS SONS AND HIS RETINUE WERE OUT ON A HUNT —

HE HASN'T SEEN THAT TIGER!

AS THE TIGER SPRANG...

+ DATTADEVI LATER BECAME THE MOTHER OF CHANDRA GUPTA II.

... A SPEAR BROUGHT IT ROARING TO THE GROUND.

SOMEONE IN OUR PARTY HAS BEEN VERY ALERT!

CHANDRA GUPTA PRETENDED TO BE ANGRY.

WHO SENT THAT SPEAR AND DENIED ME THE PRIVILEGE OF DEFENDING MYSELF?

IT WAS SAMUDRA GUPTA, FATHER.

I SHOULD HAVE KNOWN!

YOU HAVE BEEN PRESUMPTUOUS.

IGNORING KACHA'S COMMENT, SAMUDRA GUPTA ADDRESSED HIS FATHER.

I... I DID NOT MEAN TO BE AUDACIOUS, FATHER. I WAS PROTECTING THE LIFE OF MY KING.

YOU HAD NOT SEEN THE BEAST. IT COULD HAVE KILLED YOU.

THAT WAS A NARROW ESCAPE. I MUST DO WHAT I HAVE DECIDED TO DO, WITHOUT DELAY.

THE NEXT DAY, THE COURT AWAITED CHANDRA GUPTA'S ARRIVAL IN HUSHED EXPECTANCY.

WHY HAS HE CALLED THIS SPECIAL COURT?

IT MUST BE TO DISCUSS THE PLANS OF SOME CAMPAIGN.

OUR KING HAS NEVER FAVOURED A POLICY OF AGGRESSION AND EXPANSION.

THEN WHAT COULD IT BE?

THE ARRIVAL OF THE KING, HIS FAVOURITE QUEEN AND THE PRINCES PUT AN END TO THE SPECULATION.

WHEN ALL WERE SEATED —

WHAT YOU ARE ABOUT TO WITNESS TODAY MAY AMAZE SOME... DISAPPOINT A FEW... AND PLEASE MANY.

BUT WHAT I PROPOSE TO DO IS BEING DONE AFTER CAREFUL DELIBERATION AND FOR THE WELFARE OF MY SUBJECTS AND THE KINGDOM.

HE IS GOING TO PROCLAIM ME AS HIS SUCCESSOR.

I HAVE DECIDED TO WAIVE TRADITION...

?

... AND CROWN MY SON...

HE'S GOING TO ABDICATE IN MY FAVOUR!

15

The Glory of the Guptas

Script: Swarn Khandpur • Illustrations: Ramesh Umrotkar

THE RULE OF THE GUPTA DYNASTY (A.D. 320 TO 569) IS USUALLY KNOWN AS THE GOLDEN AGE OF INDIAN HISTORY. IT WAS A PERIOD OF PEACE AND PROSPERITY AND IT WITNESSED THE BLOSSOMING OF LITERATURE, SCIENCE AND THE ARTS.

IT WAS UNDER THE PATRONAGE OF THE GUPTA KINGS THAT SOME OF THE FINEST WORKS OF SANSKRIT POETRY AND DRAMA WERE WRITTEN. THE MOST FAMOUS POET AND DRAMATIST OF INDIA, KALIDASA, PROBABLY FLOURISHED DURING THIS TIME. HIS 'ABHIJNANA SHAKUNTALAM' IS WORLD-FAMOUS.

ARYABHATA, THE GREAT ASTRONOMER AND MATHEMATICIAN, WHO GAVE THE WORLD THE CONCEPT OF ZERO AND WHO WAS THE FIRST TO DISCOVER THAT THE EARTH REVOLVES ROUND THE SUN AND ROTATES ON ITS AXIS, TOO BELONGED TO THIS PERIOD.

THE IRON PILLAR AT DELHI, WHICH WEIGHS ABOUT 6 TONNES AND IS 7.32 METRES IN HEIGHT, IS A LIVING TRIBUTE TO THE GUPTA METALLURGISTS. DESPITE 2000 YEARS OF EXPOSURE TO WIND AND RAIN, IT DOES NOT HAVE EVEN A TRACE OF RUST!

ALTHOUGH MOST OF THE GUPTA KINGS WERE VAISHNAVAS, THEY WERE GENEROUS TO THE BUDDHISTS AND THE JAINS. THE AJANTA CAVES NEAR AURANGABAD WERE CARVED DURING THEIR REIGN. THE PAINTINGS ON THE WALLS, DEPICTING THE LIFE OF BUDDHA, HAVE SURVIVED TO THIS DAY.

THERE WERE SEVERAL BUDDHIST MONASTERIES WHICH WERE AIDED BY ROYAL GRANTS. THE NALANDA MONASTERY, WHICH LATER BECAME A WORLD-FAMOUS UNIVERSITY, WAS FOUNDED DURING THE GUPTA PERIOD.

LATER, WHEN THE COURTIERS WERE ALONE —

OUR KING TAKING A WIFE FROM THE LICHCHAVI OLIGARCHY IS ONE THING.

BUT MAKING A SON OF THAT UNION THE RULER IS QUITE ANOTHER. IT WAS AN UNWISE CHOICE.

ON THE CONTRARY, WITH HIM AS KING, WE CAN BE SURE OF THE CONTINUED POLITICAL AND MILITARY SUPPORT OF THE LICHCHAVIS.

THE COURTIER WHO SUPPORTED THE CHOICE WAS DHRUVABHUTI, CHIEF OF THE MILITARY AND HARISHENA'S FATHER.

WHAT IF HE ADOPTS THEIR HERETICAL CREEDS AND EN-DANGERS OUR OWN?

THE SON OF THE LICHCHAVI QUEEN SURPASSES ALL IN HIS GRASP OF THE ITIHASAS, THE DHARMA-SHASTRAS AND THE ARTHASHASTRA.

SO YOU CAN REST ASSURED THAT HIS RULE WILL BE GUIDED BY OUR TRADITIONAL VALUES.

THUS DID SAMUDRA GUPTA ASCEND THE THRONE EVEN IN THE LIFETIME OF HIS FATHER.

WHAT IS MORE, HE HAS SOUGHT THE SUPPORT OF THE NAGAS.

KACHA! MY BROTHER! TURNING TO THE NAGAS!

WHICH OF THEM?

ACHYUTSENA OF ROHILKHAND AND NAGASENA OF PADMAVATI. THE KING OF KOTA HAS JOINED THEM.

THEY ARE MARCHING TOWARDS THE CITY. KACHA HAS RIDDEN OUT TO MEET THEM.

AS THE OFFICIAL LEFT, HARISHENA BECAME THOUGHTFUL.

I HAVE HEARD FATHER SAY THAT THE NAGAS WERE NOT TOO HAPPY WITH THE POWER THE LICHCHAVI ALLIANCE GAVE US.

AND NOW THEY HOPE TO GET EVEN BY SUPPORTING FOOLISH KACHA! HMMM.

YOU ARE FIRST A KING, AND THEN THE BROTHER OF KACHA.

AND HE MUST BE PREPARED TO FIGHT EVEN HIS OWN BROTHER IN DEFENCE OF DHARMA.

SAMUDRA GUPTA SLOWLY LOOKED UP AND SMILED AT HARISHENA.

THEN HE TOOK THE BATTLE-AXE FROM HIM...

... AND STOOD UP.

I SHALL NOT TOUCH THE LUTE TILL I HAVE NO MORE USE FOR THIS. ASK DHRUVABHUTI TO SEE ME.

SOON —

DHRUVABHUTI, RALLY OUR ARMIES. THE NAGAS MUST BE QUELLED.

AND SO SAMUDRA GUPTA, AT THE HEAD OF A VAST ARMY, MARCHED OUT WITH HARISHENA, HIS FAVOURITE AT COURT.

IN THE BATTLE THAT FOLLOWED EVEN HIS ENEMIES COULD NOT HELP BUT ADMIRE HIS PROWESS IN WAR.

WE HAVE NO HOPE, ACHYUTSENA.

THE FOOL, KACHA TOLD US THAT THE SON OF THE LICHCHAVI QUEEN COULD ONLY PLUCK THE STRINGS OF A LUTE.

THOSE ARMS COULD CONTAIN AN ELEPHANT, NAGASENA. KACHA HAS MADE FOOLS OF US!

WHERE IS KACHA?

WATCHING THE TURN THE BATTLE WAS TAKING, KACHA HAD FLED FROM THE SCENE AND WAS HEARD OF NO MORE.

SAMUDRA GUPTA WON THE BATTLE AND TOOK THE THREE KINGS CAPTIVE.

I AM SPARING YOUR LIVES. BUT LET THIS BE A LESSON TO YOU. NEVER PROVOKE ME AGAIN.

THEIR TERRITORIES WERE ANNEXED TO THE GUPTA KINGDOM.

AS SAMUDRA GUPTA RODE BACK TO THE CAPITAL —

HARISHENA, ONE THING SURPRISES ME. WITH ALL THE WISDOM OUR ANCIENTS HANDED DOWN TO US, WE STILL HAVE NOT BEEN ABLE TO HAVE UNITY IN OUR LAND.

THAT COULD COME ABOUT, AS THE ARTHA-SHASTRA TEACHES US, ONLY WITH ONE STRONG IMPERIAL AUTHORITY HOLDING SWAY OVER ALL THE PETTY STATES AND TRIBAL REPUBLICS.

THEN WE SHALL BECOME THAT AUTHORITY.

SO WHEN SAMUDRA GUPTA RETURNED TO THE CAPITAL —

MAHARAJ, SHALL I BRING OUT THE LUTE?

NO, DATTADEVI, THE TIME FOR THAT IS YET TO COME.

AH, DHRUVABHUTI! HAVE YOU DRAWN UP PLANS FOR THE CAMPAIGN?

CAMPAIGN?

YES, DEAR. I AM PLANNING TO TAKE OVER THE MADRAKA, YAUDHEYA, ARJUNAYANA, PRARJUNA, MALAVA, ABHIRA, SANAKANIKA, KAKA AND KHARAPARIKA REPUBLICS.

THAT WILL BE A VERY LONG CAMPAIGN.

YES AND WILL REQUIRE MUCH PLANNING AND PREPARATION.

THEN I SHALL NOT DISTURB YOU.

AND SO BEGAN THE MASSIVE OPERATIONS PREPARATORY TO A LONG CAMPAIGN.

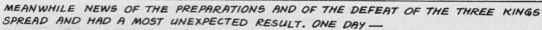

MEANWHILE NEWS OF THE PREPARATIONS AND OF THE DEFEAT OF THE THREE KINGS SPREAD AND HAD A MOST UNEXPECTED RESULT. ONE DAY —

MAHARAJ, A REPRESENTATIVE OF THE YAUDHEYAS SEEKS AN AUDIENCE.

OH! I WILL SEE HIM AT COURT.

LATER —

OUR TRIBE OFFERS YOU TRIBUTE AS OUR MOST RESPECTED OVERLORD, AND SEEKS YOUR PROTECTION AND FRIENDSHIP AT ALL TIMES.

YOUR OFFER IS ACCEPTED IF YOU AGREE NOT TO WAGE WAR AMONG YOURSELVES OR WITH ANY OTHER WHO ENJOYS OUR PROTECTION.

AN OFFICIAL OF OUR COURT WILL BE PLACED IN YOUR REPUBLIC TO ENSURE PEACE AT ALL TIMES.

OVER THE NEXT FEW MONTHS, ONE BY ONE, EACH OF THE TRIBES CAME WITH THE SAME OFFER AND WAS GIVEN THE SAME REPLY. AND SO WITHOUT A STRUGGLE, WITHOUT ANY BLOODSHED, THE TRIBES BECAME FEUDAL STATES OF THE GROWING GUPTA POWER.

WHEN THE LAST OF THE REPRESENTATIVES HAD COME AND GONE —

WHAT DO WE DO WITH ALL THE MEN WE HAVE RALLIED... ALL THE WEAPONS... ALL THE EQUIPMENT?

NOTHING IS LOST. WE STILL GO ON OUR CAMPAIGN. BUT WE TAKE A DIFFERENT ROUTE.

WE GO SOUTHWARDS INSTEAD OF WESTWARDS.

?

HARISHENA SHOOK HIS HEAD AND SMILED TO HIMSELF.

WELL, MAHARAJ. I WILL NEVER UNDERSTAND YOU.

AND SO BEGAN SAMUDRA GUPTA'S LONG MARCH SOUTHWARDS.

HE BEGAN WITH WHAT ARE NOW EASTERN MADHYA PRADESH AND NORTHERN ORISSA, MARCHED THROUGH THE HEART OF THE FORESTS OF ORISSA AND THEN ALONG THE EASTERN COAST TO THE KINGDOM OF THE PALLAVAS, CONQUERING EVERY KINGDOM ON HIS ROUTE.

AS HE WAS PREPARING TO MARCH FURTHER SOUTH, NEWS CAME FROM THE NORTH.

MAHARAJ, ACHYUTSENA AND NAGASENA ARE PLANNING AN UPRISING. THEY HAVE ALLIED THEMSELVES WITH SIX OTHER NAGA RAJAS UNDER GANAPATINAGA OF MATHURA.

SAMUDRA GUPTA WAS QU'ET FOR A WHILE AS HE DID SOME QUICK REASONING. THEN —

HARISHENA. WE ARE TURNING BACK.

OUR CAMPAIGN WAS SUCCESSFUL. BUT STAYING BACK TO CONSOLIDATE OUR POSITION IS NOT POSSIBLE. NOT NOW, NOR IN THE FUTURE.

I HAVE DECIDED TO REINSTATE THE KINGS WITH ALL POWERS AND SETTLE FOR AN ANNUAL TRIBUTE FROM THEM.

SAMUDRA GUPTA RETRACED HIS ROUTE...

...SET THE KINGS BACK ON THEIR THRONES, ON HIS TERMS...

... AND AT LAST REACHED HIS CAPITAL TO MAKE PREPARATIONS FOR THE BATTLE AHEAD.

HARISHENA, I HAVE MADE UP MY MIND.

ABOUT WHAT NOW?

WE WILL ATTACK THE NAGAS BEFORE THEY ATTACK US. I HAVE BEEN TOO LENIENT WITH THEM.

THEY ARE A SERIOUS THREAT TO OUR DREAMS OF AN EMPIRE OF PEACE AND PLENTY.

THIS TIME I WILL EXTERMINATE THEM, PERFORM AN ASHWAMEDHA SACRIFICE AND ESTABLISH THE SUZERAINTY OF OUR EMPIRE.

AND TRUE TO HIS WORD, HE RUTHLESSLY ATTACKED AND SLEW THE OFFENDERS...

... TOOK OVER THEIR ARMIES AND ANNEXED THEIR TERRITORIES.

ON RETURNING TO HIS CAPITAL, HE PERFORMED THE ASHWAMEDHA SACRIFICE, TO WHICH KINGS FROM PARTS OF AFGHANISTAN, PERSIA, SRI LANKA AND SOUTH-EAST ASIA SENT THEIR ENVOYS WITH GIFTS.

MEGHAVARNA, THE KING OF SRI LANKA, EVEN SOUGHT PERMISSION TO BUILD MONASTERIES FOR THE SRI LANKA BUDDHISTS IN SAMUDRA GUPTA'S EMPIRE. IT WAS READILY GRANTED.

WHEN ALL THE RITUALS AND FESTIVITIES CAME TO AN END —

MAHARAJ!

IN THE LAST TEN YEARS OF HIS REIGN, SAMUDRA GUPTA SAW HIS DREAM BECOME A REALITY. THE ORDER AND STABILITY HE HAD BROUGHT ABOUT, PAVED THE WAY FOR CHANDRA GUPTA II, HIS SON BORN OF DATTADEVI, TO CARRY THE GUPTA GLORY TO ITS ZENITH. LITERATURE AND THE ARTS FLOURISHED, EARNING THE GUPTA AGE THE EPITHET "GOLDEN".

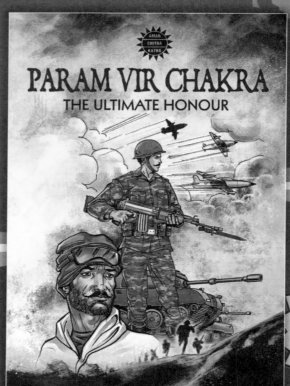

HARSHA

A GALLANT KING OF KANAUJ

The route to your roots

HARSHA

Starting off as the ruler of tiny Thaneshwar, Harsha (7th century AD) rose to become the powerful monarch of the kingdom of Kanauj. He avenged the wicked assassination of his elder brother and the cowardly abduction of his sister. His biographer Bana Bhatta and the Chinese traveller Hiuen Tsang were unanimous in their praise of this learned king, whose fame did much to create a glowing image of India in lands far away.

<table>
<tr><td>**Script**</td><td>**Illustrations**</td><td>**Editor**</td></tr>
<tr><td>Yagya Sharma
Anand Prakash Singh</td><td>Madhu Powle</td><td>Anant Pai</td></tr>
</table>

ABOUT 1,400 YEARS AGO, THANESHWAR, A POWERFUL KINGDOM IN NORTHERN INDIA WAS RULED BY PRABHAKAR VARDHAN. DURING THIS PERIOD THE HUNS HAD STARTED HARASSING THE PEOPLE OF THANESHWAR. SO THE KING SENT HIS ABLE SONS TO PUNISH THEM.

WHILE HUNTING FAR AWAY FROM THE CAMP, HARSHA SAW SOMEBODY RIDING TOWARDS HIM.

HE SEEMS TO BE IN A GREAT HURRY.

PRINCE HARSHA, YOUR FATHER IS VERY ILL. HE WANTS TO SEE YOU AND PRINCE RAJYA.

I'LL GO TO HIM. YOU INFORM MY BROTHER.

BOTH PRINCES RUSHED TO THANESHWAR, BUT THEY WERE TOO LATE.

YOUR FATHER WAS A NOBLE KING.

A FEW DAYS LATER—

PRINCE RAJYA, YOU WILL NOW HAVE TO SIT ON THE THRONE.

OH, NO! LET HARSHA BE THE KING.

RAJYASHRI, THEIR SISTER, WAS WORRIED. SHE TALKED
TO HER HUSBAND GRAHAVARMAN, THE KING OF KANNAUJ.

MEANWHILE, DEVGUPTA, THE GREEDY KING OF MALWA WAS BUSY PLOTTING.

THE TIME IS RIPE. WE CAN NOW GRAB THE KINGDOMS OF THANESHWAR AND KANNAUJ.

BUT THEY ARE VERY POWERFUL, SIR.

I KNOW. BUT IF WE KILL GRAHA-VARMAN, THE INEXPERIENCED RAJYAVARDHAN WILL NOT BE ABLE TO DEFEND BOTH KINGDOMS.

BUT HOW ARE WE GOING TO KILL GRAHAVARMAN?

I HAVE A PLAN. DURING THE SPRING FESTIVAL, WE WILL DISGUISE OUR-SELVES AS SIMPLE PEASANTS AND MINGLE WITH THE COMMONERS OF KANNAUJ. WHEN GRAHAVARMAN COMES TO CELEBRATE THE FESTIVAL WITH HIS PEOPLE, WE WILL KILL HIM.

ACCORDING TO THEIR PLAN, DEVGUPTA AND HIS SOLDIERS DRESSED IN ORDINARY CLOTHES, MINGLED WITH THE PEOPLE OF KANNAUJ. THEN AS KING GRAHAVARMAN WAS ENTERING A TEMPLE –

AFTER KILLING GRAHAVARMAN, DEVGUPTA FORCIBLY CARRIED RAJYASHRI WITH HIM.

HELP! HELP!

THE NEWS OF DEVGUPTA'S TREACHERY REACHED RAJYAVARDHAN.

MAHARAJ, KING DEVGUPTA OF MALWA, HAS CARRIED AWAY YOUR SISTER.

DEVGUPTA HAS INVITED HIS DEATH.

7

MAHARAJ, ALLOW ME TO ATTACK MALWA.

NO, HARSHA!

BEING THE ELDER BROTHER AND THE KING IT IS MY DUTY TO DO SO.

YOU HAVE BEHAVED LIKE A COWARD.

MEANWHILE IN MALWA—

SAY WHATEVER YOU LIKE. BUT I SHALL SOON BE THE KING OF KANNAUJ AS WELL AS THANESHWAR.

IMPRISON HER. LET HER LEARN TO RESPECT A KING.

THE SIGHTS IN THE PRISON DISTURBED RAJYASHRI.

THE PAINFUL CRIES OF OTHER PRISONERS AGONISED HER HEART AND SOUL.

OH, MY GOD!

WHILE RAJYASHRI WAS SUFFERING MENTALLY, DEVGUPTA WAS ENJOYING HIMSELF.

JUST THEN DEVGUPTA RECEIVED A MESSAGE.

RAJYAVARDHAN IS PREPARING TO ATTACK US, SIR!

I EXPECTED THIS. GO AND CALL KING SHASHANK OF GAUD. I WANT TO TALK TO HIM.

VERY SOON DEVGUPTA WAS SCHEMING WITH SHASHANK.

I WILL SHARE HALF OF THE KINGDOMS OF THANE- SHWAR AND KANNAUJ WITH YOU IF YOU HELP ME.

I WILL. WHAT MUST I DO?

WIN RAJYAVARDHAN'S CONFIDENCE AND ACCOMPANY HIM IN HIS ATTACK ON ME.

WHEN THE BATTLE BEGINS, ATTACK RAJYAVARDHAN FROM THE REAR. ONCE HE IS DEAD, WE'VE AS GOOD AS WON.

YOUR PLAN IS EXCELLENT. WE SHALL DEFINITELY SUCCEED.

BECAUSE OF THE BATTLE, EVERYTHING WAS DISORGANISED IN DEVGUPTA'S PRISON.

WE NEED ALL THE SOLDIERS. LEAVE ONLY ONE MAN TO GUARD THE PRISON.

THE SOLDIER LEFT TO GUARD THE PRISON, POSSESSED A NOBLE HEART.

THIS SECRET PASSAGE WILL CARRY YOU TO THE JUNGLE.

THANK YOU. YOU ARE VERY NOBLE. PLEASE TAKE CARE OF YOURSELF.

THUS RAJYASHRI ESCAPED FROM DEVGUPTA'S PRISON.

DEVGUPTA'S SOLDIERS WERE PATROLLING THE JUNGLE, BUT LUCKILY SHE WAS NOT SPOTTED BY THEM.

FINALLY RAJYASHRI ESCAPED INTO THE JUNGLE.

MEANWHILE RAJYAVARDHAN FOUGHT FIERCELY. SHASHANK WAS HELPLESS AS HE WAS SURROUNDED BY RAJYAVARDHAN'S PERSONAL GUARDS.

FINALLY RAJYAVARDHAN KILLED DEVGUPTA AND WON THE BATTLE.

VICTORY TO MAHARAJ RAJYA-VARDHAN.

SHASHANK WAS VERY UPSET OVER THE DEATH OF DEVGUPTA.

WITH DEV-GUPTA'S DEATH, MY DREAMS ARE ALSO SHATTERED.

BUT IF I SOMEHOW KILL RAJYAVARDHAN, HIS KINGDOM WILL BECOME WEAK AND THEN I SHALL GRAB IT EASILY.

NOW WE SHOULD MAKE PLANS FOR THE FUTURE. PLEASE COME TO MY TENT TONIGHT.

I WILL COME.

THAT NIGHT IN SHASHANK'S TENT —

NOW I MUST ESCAPE IMMEDIATELY.

IN THE COURT OF THANESHWAR —

SIR, MAHARAJ RAJYAVARDHAN HAS BEEN KILLED TREACHEROUSLY BY SHASHANK.

SHASHANK SHALL PAY FOR THIS!

AND SIR, MAHARANI RAJYASHRI HAS ESCAPED FROM THE PRISON BUT NOBODY KNOWS WHERE SHE HAS GONE.

SEND MESSENGERS IN ALL DIRECTIONS TO FIND HER.

HARSHA THEN MARCHED WITH A HUGE FORCE TO PUNISH KING SHASHANK.

SHASHANK HAD NEVER THOUGHT THAT YOUNG HARSHA COULD ORGANISE SUCH A LARGE FORCE.

ONE DAY HE WILL DIE A DOG'S DEATH BUT JUST NOW I MUST FIND MY SISTER RAJYASHRI.

MAHARAJ, THE COWARDLY SHASHANK HAS RUN AWAY INTO THE JUNGLES.

SIR, A MESSENGER HAS BROUGHT SOME NEWS ABOUT MAHARANI RAJYASHRI.

BRING HIM IN AT ONCE.

HARSHA WAS RETURNING HOME AFTER CONQUERING KATHIAWAR. HIS SOLDIERS WERE TIRED AND EAGER TO REACH HOME.

AND AT THAT MOMENT PULAKESHIN ATTACKED HARSHA.

THE FIGHTING CONTINUED FOR SEVERAL DAYS. LOSSES WERE HEAVY ON BOTH SIDES.

HARSHA'S TIRED SOLDIERS HAD TO RETREAT. HE WAS VERY SAD.

ALL THOSE MEN WERE KILLED FOR NOTHING.

SOMETIME LATER IN THANESHWAR—

MAHARAJ HARSHA, LET US ATTACK PULAKESHIN. THIS TIME WE ARE FULLY PREPARED TO CRUSH HIM.

I HAVE HAD ENOUGH OF THIS BLOOD-SHED.

TO FULFIL HIS DREAM, HARSHA GAVE FINANCIAL HELP TO THE POOR.

HE APPOINTED PHYSICIANS TO TREAT THE SICK FREE OF COST.

HE HELPED STUDENTS TO PURSUE THEIR STUDIES.

DURING HIS TIME, TRADERS CAME FROM AS FAR AS CHINA.

PEOPLE PROSPERED.

AND FOLLOWERS OF DIFFERENT FAITHS LIVED IN PEACE AND HARMONY.

DURING THIS PERIOD, HIUEN TSANG, THE FAMOUS CHINESE PILGRIM AND SCHOLAR CAME TO INDIA. AFTER SPENDING SOME TIME IN EASTERN INDIA, HE MET HARSHA.

MAHARAJ, A BUDDHIST MONK WANTS TO SEE YOU.

BRING HIM IN.

WELCOME, SCHOLAR HIUEN TSANG. I WAS LOOKING FORWARD TO MEETING YOU.

MAHARAJ, I AM HONOURED.

SIR, I HAVE COME HERE TO LEARN MORE ABOUT THE BUDDHIST RELIGION.

I HOPE, YOU FIND YOUR STAY COMFORTABLE

HIUEN TSANG STAYED IN INDIA FOR A FEW YEARS.

DURING HIUEN TSANG'S STAY, HARSHA DECIDED TO HOLD A SEMINAR ON RELIGIONS.

MINISTER, PLEASE INVITE SCHOLARS OF DIFFERENT RELIGIONS TO TAKE PART IN THIS SEMINAR.

EMINENT SCHOLARS OF HINDUISM, JAINISM AND BUDDHISM CAME TO PARTICIPATE IN THE SEMINAR.

THE SEMINAR CONTINUED FOR SEVERAL DAYS.

HIUEN TSANG TOO PARTICIPATED IN THE SEMINAR.

ACHARYA HIUEN TSANG, YOU ARE THE MOST NOBLE SCHOLAR I HAVE EVER KNOWN.

BUT SOME OF THE GREEDY PARTICIPANTS DID NOT LIKE THAT A FOREIGNER SHOULD BE PRAISED BY THIER KING.

IF HIUEN TSANG MAKES A GOOD IMPRESSION ON THE KING, WE MAY NOT GET THOSE RICH REWARDS, WE EXPECT.

YES, HE MUST BE FINISHED BEFORE HE DOES MORE HARM.

BUT THIS CONSPIRACY WAS REPORTED TO HARSHA IMMEDIATELY.

I WARN THE CONSPIRATORS THAT ANYBODY WHO TRIES TO HARM ACHARYA HIUEN TSANG SHALL BE PUNISHED. PROCLAIM THIS TO ALL.

I BELIEVE IN NON-VIOLENCE, THE POOR AND THE WEAK SHALL BE PROTECTED. THOSE WHO PREACH VIOLENCE SHALL PAY FOR IT WITH THEIR OWN LIVES.

AS A RESULT OF THIS STERN WARNING, NOBODY TRIED TO HARM HIUEN TSANG.

THE SEMINAR IS OVER. THE SCHOLARS SHOULD NOW BE PRESENTED WITH GIFTS.

THE ARRANGEMENTS HAVE BEEN MADE, MAHARAJ!

SOON THE GIFTS BROUGHT FOR DONATION WERE EXHAUSTED. BUT STILL MANY PEOPLE REMAINED WITHOUT GIFTS.

BRING ALL THE REMAINING WEALTH FROM THE ROYAL TREASURY.

AS YOU WISH, MAHARAJ.

THE ROYAL WEALTH WAS ALSO GIVEN AWAY BUT EVEN THEN SOME PEOPLE WERE LEFT OUT.

HERE TAKE MY ORNAMENTS. OF WHAT USE ARE THEY IF MY PEOPLE LIVE IN MISERY.

IN THE END ONLY ONE MAN WAS LEFT OUT.

I AM SORRY THAT NOTHING IS LEFT WITH ME EXCEPT THE CLOTHES I AM WEARING. PLEASE ACCEPT THEM.

In this manner, every five years, Harsha gave away all his wealth to the scholars, the priests and the poor.